Let's Play Tag!

📖 Read the Page

▶️ Read the Story

⭐ Game

🔶 Sound It / Say It

🔄 Repeat

⏹️ Stop

Get-Ready Words

Beast	Lumiere
beauty	mirror
Belle	prince
book	rose
castle	spell

Beauty and the Beast

The Enchanted Rose

 Belle and her father live in a small town. She likes to read books. He likes to make things.

"You will win first prize at the fair!" Belle says.

Belle's father goes to the fair.

But Belle's father gets lost.

She finds his hat. It is outside the Beast's castle!

"Please let him go," Belle says. "I will take his place."

"Then you must stay here forever," says the Beast.

Belle says that she will stay.

The Beast is a prince under a spell.

He must learn to love another and earn her love in return. If he doesn't, he will be a beast forever.

The Beast's friends are under a spell, too.

"So nice to meet you, my dear!" says Lumiere.

He and his friends put on a show for Belle.

"The castle is your home now," Lumiere says. "But there is one rule. Do not go to the west wing."

But Belle wants to see the west wing.

The Beast finds her.

"Stop!" he roars.

The Beast grabs the rose.

Belle runs away, but five big wolves stop her!

The Beast saves her, but he is hurt.

"Let me help you," she says to him.

Belle and the Beast become friends.

 The Beast shows Belle his books.

She smiles. "Oh, I love books!"

"I know," says the Beast.

The Beast learns to be nice.

He loves Belle. He has never felt like this.

But does she love him?

 Belle learns her father is sick.

"He needs me," she says.

"Then you must go," says the Beast.

He gives Belle a gift. It is a magic mirror.

Belle goes home to help her father.

At home, Belle looks in the magic mirror. The Beast is hurt! He needs help!

Belle goes back to the castle. She hopes she can make it in time.

"Please don't leave me!" says Belle. "I love you."

The spell is broken!

The Beast turns back into a prince.

"Belle, it's me," he says.

Belle can see it is true. She smiles. "It is you!"

The prince learns what true beauty is.

True beauty comes from the heart.

The End

Words You're Learning

Short Vowels

Short a Words	Short e Words	Short i Words	Short o Words	Short u Words
and	get	big	not	but
at	help	it	on	must
can	let	will	stop	run
grab	west			under
hat				

Long Vowels

Long a Words	Long e Words	Long i Words	Long o Words	Long u Words
make	beast	like	home	rule
place	leave	nice	hope	true
stay	meet	smile	rose	
		time		

Sight Words

are	one	want
come	the	what
do	there	you
does	to